Walk Around

By Ken Neubeck
Color by Don Greer
Illustrated by Richard Hudson

A-10 Warthog

GW00771654

Walk Around Number 17

squadron/signal publications

Introduction

The Fairchild Republic A-10 Thunderbolt II, more commonly known as the Warthog, is the only aircraft in the US Air Force arsenal that is built solely for the mission of close air support. The A-10 was designed as an aerial counter to the large number of Warsaw Pact tanks and other armored vehicles that were stationed in eastern Europe during the 1970s and 1980s. Production of the A-10 began in 1975 and, when the assembly lines had closed, 715 had been built (including the two prototypes).

The A-10 is quite simply an aircraft that is built around a gun. That gun is a seven barreled, 30 mm GAU-8/A automatic cannon designed by General Electric. The weapon fires rounds with spent uranium tips at a rate of seven rounds per second. These rounds are capable of penetrating the upper armor of any tank.

The A-10 is powered by two turbofan engines located on pylons above the aft fuselage as part of a series of built-in survival features against hostile ground fire. Another survival feature is the titanium 'bathtub' armor that surrounds the cockpit and protects the pilot.

By 1990 the A-10 was headed for an early retirement. The Air Force was looking into using modified F-16 Fighting Falcons in the close support role. Additional mission specific equipment was to be added to the F-16 in order to improve its low level attack capabilities. Additionally, the F-16 would retain much of its air-to-air combat capabilities — an option the A-10 as a dedicated close support aircraft did not have. Before this happened, hostilities broke out in the Middle East when Iraq invaded Kuwait. Squadrons of A-10s from five different bases were deployed to the region in August of 1990. The A-10 saw extensive action in several roles during OPERATION DESERT STORM in early 1991: SCUD missile hunter, rescue mission support, artillery post attacks, and of course, its primary role of tank killer.

Conservative estimates place the number of tanks being destroyed by the A-10 as almost 1,000, but the numbers are likely much higher. US Air Force experimentation with F-16s in the ground attack role demonstrated that the Fighting Falcon was simply too fast and fragile for the role in which the A-10 had been specifically designed. There were also a number of high profile events during the war when A-10s, suffering severe battle damage, were able to return to base. Six A-10s were lost during the Gulf War which, considering their low level and dangerous mission, is surprisingly low.

About 350 A-10s are still in service with the USAF, USAF Reserve, and Air National Guard units since no suitable replacement for the close air support mission exists at this time. These aircraft are expected to be in the USAF inventory well beyond the year 2020. The A-10 'Warthog' is a common sight at air shows and open house events at Air Force bases around the country.

Acknowledgements

Anthony Abbott
A. Antonivk
Jim Boss
Daniel Brown
Dave Conroe
John Golden
Dennis R. Jenkins
Curtiss Knowles
Ken Kubik
R. Leonard
Pete Nelson

Robert V. Pease
C. Reed
Fred Schlenker III
Joshua Stoff
Willa Talton
Robin Van Dorst

Cradle of Aviation Museum, Mitchel Field, Long Island
Empire State Air Museum, Schenectady, NY
Fairchild Republic Archives
USAF

ISBN 0-89747-400-7

If you have any photographs of aircraft, armor, soldiers or ships of any nation, particularly wartime snapshots, why not share them with us and help make Squadron/Signal's books all the more interesting and complete in the future. Any photograph sent to us will be copied and the original returned. The donor will be fully credited for any photos used. Please send them to:

Squadron/Signal Publications, Inc.
1115 Crowley Drive
Carrollton, TX 75011-5010

Если у вас есть фотографии самолетов, вооружения, солдат или кораблей любой страны, особенно, снимки времён войны, поделитесь с нами и помогите сделать новые книги издательства Эскадрон/Сигнал ещё интереснее. Мы переснимем ваши фотографии и вернём оригиналы. Имена приславших снимки будут сопровождать все опубликованные фотографии. Пожалуйста, присылайте фотографии по адресу:

Squadron/Signal Publications, Inc.
1115 Crowley Drive
Carrollton, TX 75011-5010

軍用機、装甲車両、兵士、軍艦などの写真を所持しておられる方はいらっしゃいませんか？どの国のものでも結構です。作戦中に撮影されたものが特に良いのです。Squadron/Signal社の出版する刊行物において、このような写真は内容を一層充実し、興味深くすることができます。当方にお送り頂いた写真は、複写の後お返しいたします。出版物中に写真を使用した場合は、必ず提供者のお名前を明記させて頂きます。お写真は下記にご送付ください。

Squadron/Signal Publications, Inc.
1115 Crowley Drive
Carrollton, TX 75011-5010

(Front Cover) An A-10 is refueled during a quick turn-around at a Saudi air base during the opening rounds of OPERATION DESERT STORM in January of 1991

(Overleaf) With its In-flight refueling receptacle open, an A-10 Warthog, closes on a USAF tanker during OPERATION DESERT STORM in January of 1991. The 'Hog is carrying two AGM-65 Maverick missiles, a pair of AIM-9 Sidewinder air-to-air missiles, and an ALQ-119 electronic counter measures pod.

(Back Cover) Now a combat veteran, an A-10 of the 23rd Tactical Fighter Wing (Provisional) rolls in to attack retreating Iraqi armor during the waning days of OPERATION DESERT STORM in late February of 1991.

The A-10 prototype's TF-34 turbofan engines were powered up for the first time in 1972. This airframe mounted a 20mm M61 Vulcan cannon due to the unavailability of the 30mm GAU-8/A cannon at the time. (Fairchild Republic Archives)

Both nacelle access doors were left open when the engines were powered up in 1972. The clamshell doors were designed to allow easy access to the engines. (Fairchild Republic Archives)

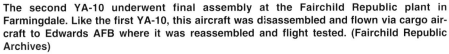

The second YA-10 underwent final assembly at the Fairchild Republic plant in Farmingdale. Like the first YA-10, this aircraft was disassembled and flown via cargo aircraft to Edwards AFB where it was reassembled and flight tested. (Fairchild Republic Archives)

The 30mm GAU-8/A cannon replaced the smaller and less powerful 20mm cannon at Edwards AFB. The A-10 was originally designed to mount the larger weapon, however, the gun was not ready in time to be fitted at the factory. (Fairchild Republic Archives)

(Above) A completed wing assembly consisted of the center wing box, two outer wing panels, and the landing gear pods. The weapons pylons were separate fittings and added later. Much of the interior and exterior components were coated with a zinc chromate yellow primer. (Ken Neubeck)

(Above Left) Fuselage and wing assemblies were completed at the Fairchild Republic plant in Farmingdale, NY. The wings and fuselages were then shipped by truck to the Hagerstown, Maryland facility for final assembly, painting, and flight testing. (Fairchild Republic Archives)

(Left) An A-10 fuselage and its wings are prepared for shipment to the Hagerstown, Maryland plant. Aircraft skins were given a thin coat of zinc chromate yellow to inhibit corrosion. The final camouflage scheme was applied after the airframe was complete. (Fairchild Republic Archives)

The A-10 final assembly line was located in the Fairchild Republic plant in Hagerstown, Maryland. The next stop for these airframes is the paint shop where the camouflage paint scheme will be applied. Production peaked at 12 aircraft per month during the early 1980s. (Fairchild Republic Archives)

(Above) The first A-10 prototype (31669) was designated the YA-10. Both engines were mounted high on the aft fuselage where their exhaust plumes could be masked by the horizontal and vertical stabilizers. The fairing on the upper starboard portion of the nose is a mount for an instrumentation boom. The A-10 competed against the Northrop A-9 ina flyoff for the close air support (CAS) role. The A-10 was declared the winner of the flyoff in January of 1973. (Fairchild Republic Archives)

(Above Left) The A-10 prototype, still equipped with the 20mm M61 Vulcan cannon, but wearing a new camouflage scheme, undergoes a pre-flight check at Edwards AFB in 1973. The 30mm GAU-8/A was not ready until after flight testing had begun. (Fairchild Republic Archives)

(Left) The YA-10 prototype was reassembled at Edwards AFB for flight testing over the California desert. A Fairchild Republic Company test pilot completes his final checks before conducting a test flight at Edwards AFB. This aircraft is equipped with the McDonnell-Douglas ESCAPAC ejection seat. Later production Warthogs would be equipped with the ACES II system. (Fairchild Republic Archives)

(Above) The YA-10 prototype was tied down in order to test fire the newly installed 30mm cannon at a reinforced bunker at Edwards AFB. The YA-10 was also equipped with a lower fin cap having a straight leading edge. The straight edge eventually gave way to the curved lower fin cap seen on production A-10s. (Fairchild Republic Archives)

(Above Right) The second Development Test & Evaluation (DT&E) aircraft lifts off from the Fairchild Republic facility for its delivery flight to Edwards AFB in early 1975. This was the first A-10 to fly out of the plant and the first to conduct a cross-country flight. (Fairchild Republic Archives)

(Right) An A-10 undergoes assembly on the final production line in the Fairchild Republic plant in Hagerstown, Maryland. A number of the access doors are open, both on the side of the aircraft and beneath the fuselage in order to install additional equipment. These same doors allowed easy access and maintenance in the field. (Fairchild Republic Archives)

A Warthog pilot sits well forward in the aircraft and has exceptional visibility from the cockpit. The cockpit is situated inside a titanium armor 'bathtub' that is located immediately above the 30mm gun and nose wheel well. The GAU-8/A ammunition drum is buried within the fuselage behind and below the cockpit.

(Above) Flush rivets and quick-turn fasteners are used around the forward fuselage to improve aerodynamics and allow rapid access to the fuselage equipment bays. This A-10 (82-662) was transferred from the 23rd TFW to the 353rd TFS during OPERATION DESERT STORM where it received new artwork in the form of a Sylvester cartoon. The 23rd TFW's traditional tigermouth marking was removed. (Anthony Abbott)

(Above Right) ALR-69 Radar Warning Receiver (RWR) antennas are located on both sides of the nose. The antenna mount is missing its dome cover. The ALR-69 system provides the pilot with the approximate range and bearing of threat emitters such as those associated with a surface-to-air (SAM) missile tracking radar. A second pair of antennas is located on the tail cone. (Ken Neubeck)

(Right) Warthog nose art is a popular addition to A-10 paint schemes. The ALR-69 RWR antenna covers provide a convenient location to depict the nostrils. This A-10 was part of the 47th Tactical Fighter Squadron at Barksdale AFB, Louisiana. (Ken Kubik)

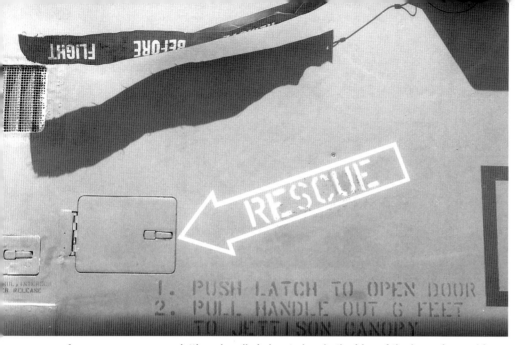

An emergency canopy jettison handle is located on both sides of the lower forward fuselage. The handle is covered by this door. The door is finger activated by pushing in on the latch.

This is the port side emergency canopy release door and handle. In the event of an emergency, a groundcrew member grabs the handle, pulls the line out six feet, then pulls hard in order to jettison the canopy. (Ken Neubeck)

A series of vents on the forward fuselage sides cools the avionics bays and purges the interior of gases that are built up when the gun is fired.

Additional vents surround the door covering the cockpit ladder bay. The door and ladder are spring loaded to open and extend simply by pushing a button. A magnet holds the open door against the fuselage.

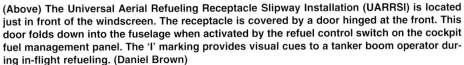

(Above) The Universal Aerial Refueling Receptacle Slipway Installation (UARRSI) is located just in front of the windscreen. The receptacle is covered by a door hinged at the front. This door folds down into the fuselage when activated by the refuel control switch on the cockpit fuel management panel. The 'I' marking provides visual cues to a tanker boom operator during in-flight refueling. (Daniel Brown)

(Above Right) The UARRSI interior is painted white. Both the door and the fixed upper plate on this receptacle have been removed. Other components have also been removed giving the receptacle a bare look. When the tanker boom is inserted into the receptacle, the nozzle latch rollers are moved into the locked position and the fuel transfer begins. (Ken Neubeck)

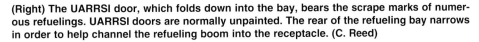

(Right) The UARRSI door, which folds down into the bay, bears the scrape marks of numerous refuelings. UARRSI doors are normally unpainted. The rear of the refueling bay narrows in order to help channel the refueling boom into the receptacle. (C. Reed)

(Above) The refueling boom is long enough to keep the A-10, as well as most other aircraft, out of the tanker's wake turbulence. The receiving pilots only have to stay within a specific area behind and below the tanker — the boom operator does the rest by 'flying' the boom into the UARRSI. (C. Knowles)

A-10 Fuel Capacities

The A-10 has four (4) internal fuel tanks — two in the fuselage and one in each wing center section. The two fuel tanks in the fuselage are known as the left and right main tanks although they are actually mounted fore-and-aft in the center fuselage between the cockpit and engines. Additionally, the A-10 can carry three external fuel tanks on the centerline and inboard wing pylons.

LEFT MAIN (FWD) TANK	511 Gallons
RIGHT MAIN (AFT) TANK	511 Gallons
LEFT WING TANK	311 Gallons
RIGHT WING TANK	311 Gallons
CENTERLINE (EXT) TANK	600 Gallons
LEFT WING (EXT) TANK	600 Gallons
RIGHT WING (EXT) TANK	600 Gallons
TOTAL FUEL	3444 Gallons

(Left) A KC-10 refueling boom is plugged into the refueling receptacle of an A-10. Fuel can be transferred into any of the A-10's fuel tanks via a series of switches in the cockpit. When each tank is filled, pilot valves cause fuel shut-off valves within each tank to close, preventing fuel overspill. (C. Knowles)

(Above) A Wayne Colony automatic loader is used to feed the GAU-8/A's 30mm rounds into the ammunition drum. The power loader allows a faster turn around time in combat conditions. The A-10 was designed to fly several combat sorties per day — often from unimproved forward air strips or stretches of highway. (Ken Kubik)

(Above Right) Ground crew members assigned to the Massachusetts Air National Guard use the automatic power loader to feed 30mm rounds into the GAU-8/A cannon. The ammunition drum is housed within the fuselage behind and below the cockpit. (Ken Kubik)

(Right) The GAU-8/A weapon system consists of a seven-barreled 30mm gun, ammunition feed chutes, gun and ammunition drives, and the ammunition drum. The A-10 can expend its full complement of 1175-1350 rounds in less than one minute at the high fire rate setting. (Ken Kubik)

13

The A-10 was designed to use the GAU-8/A Avenger rotary cannon from the outset. The large, heavy weapon required some sophisticated packaging to get everything to fit and work, and yet still allow easy access for ground crews. The interior of the gun bay is painted Aircraft Gray (FS16473) (Ken Kubik)

Several removable or hinged panels provide easy access to the GAU-8/A weapon, feed chutes, and drum magazine. The gun can be worked on *in situ* or dropped out the bottom of the aircraft if necessary. (Fairchild Republic Archives)

The power loader is attached to the ammunition feed panel located below the cockpit. The power loader feeds the rounds into the ammunition drum as well as pulls out the spent 30mm cartridge cases which are returned to the drum after firing. (Ken Kubik)

The automatic gun loader is equipped with articulated arms and a mobile carriage to allow the weapon to be loaded from a variety of positions and angles. (Fairchild Republic Archives)

A power drive unit pulls rounds from the ammunition drum and feeds them into the cannon's breech assembly while a second drive unit turns the gun. The gun and its drive and ammunition feed units are mounted to the left of the aircraft centerline. (Fairchild Republic Archives)

The seven barrels of the 30mm gun are contained within a shroud faired into the lower nose of the A-10. The scoop below the nose ducts additional air into the gun bay. This air, mixed with gun gases and contaminants, is then pulled out via a series of louvers along the port fuselage side. (R. Van Dorst)

Circular holes in the barrel sleeve provide additional cooling air for the seven gun barrels. The nut in the front plate has been safety wired in place. The entire assembly rotates when the gun is fired. The rifling inside the barrels extends to the muzzle — flash suppressors are not fitted. (Ken Neubeck)

A pinwheel device, developed by Battelle Laboratories, was attached to the front of the gun on a Development Test & Evaluation aircraft in order to disperse the gun gases and prevent their entry into the engines. This device was used on a number of A-10s, but it caused additional vibrations which led to cracks in the forward fuselage structure. The device was eventually discarded. (Fairchild Republic Archives)

The gun is mounted slightly to the left of the aircraft centerline, however, the *firing* barrel is on the centerline to prevent the recoil from skewing the aircraft off the target. (R. Van Dorst)

The nose gear is mounted to the right of the gun and the aircraft centerline. The single wheel nose gear unit is fully steerable and retracts forward into the well using a single rear mounted hydraulic ram. The nose wheel tire is 24 inches in diameter. Both the tire and wheel are manufactured by Goodyear Aerospace. (C. Knowles)

The nose gear mounts a landing light (top) and a taxi light (bottom). The landing light is fixed, however, the taxi light turns to follow the steerable nose wheel. The hydraulic nose wheel steering unit is mounted on the front of the strut between the two lights.

The forward retracting, offset nose gear is fully enclosed within the wheel well. The center wall separates the landing gear compartment from the gun compartment. This aircraft is also missing the forward wheel well door. The nose gear strut and well are painted Aircraft Gray (FS16473), although some aircraft have had gloss white used in this area. (C. Knowles)

The nose gear strut is hinged at the rear strut well bulkhead. A single hydraulic ram (not visible) immediately behind the strut pushes the strut up into the well when the gear is retracted. (R. Van Dorst)

The single nosewheel is contained within the narrow confines of the forward nosewheel compartment. Components of the cockpit environmental control system are also contained within the well. This portion of the nose wheel well is covered by a single, side hinging door. (R. Van Dorst)

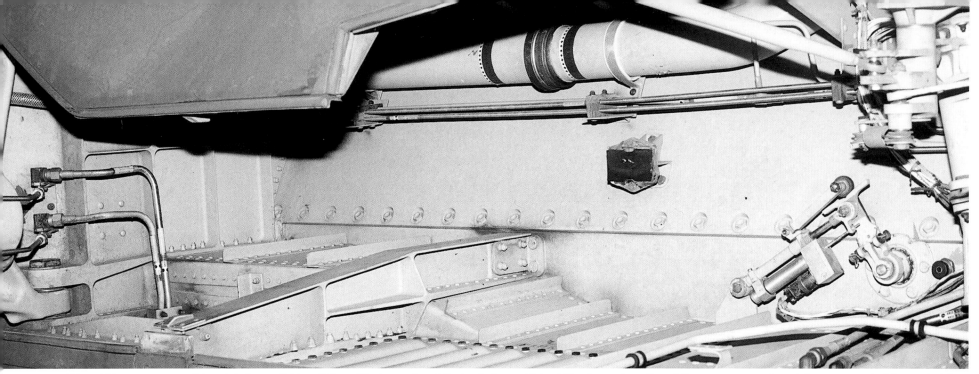

(Above) The nose gear well is painted overall Aircraft Gray. The large pipe at the top is the fuel transfer pipe leading from the Universal Aerial Refueling Receptacle Slipway Installation (UARRSI) to the main fuel tanks in the center fuselage section. (C. Knowles)

(Below) The forward section of the nose gear well contains a maze of wiring and piping. At left is the retraction mechanism for the side hinging wheel well door, however, the door has been removed from this aircraft. The door hinge slot is visible at upper right. (C. Knowles)

The hydraulic nose gear steering unit was built by Teledyne Hydra Power of California, while the nose gear strut assembly was manufactured by Menasco of Canada. The A-10 is capable of performing a 180˚ turn within the confines of a runway only fifty feet wide. (Ken Neubeck)

The nose wheel mounts a 24-inch Goodyear tire. The A-10 landing gear struts were originally painted white, but light gray is now common. The inner face of the nose gear aft door provides a convenient space for individual artwork. (Ken Kubik)

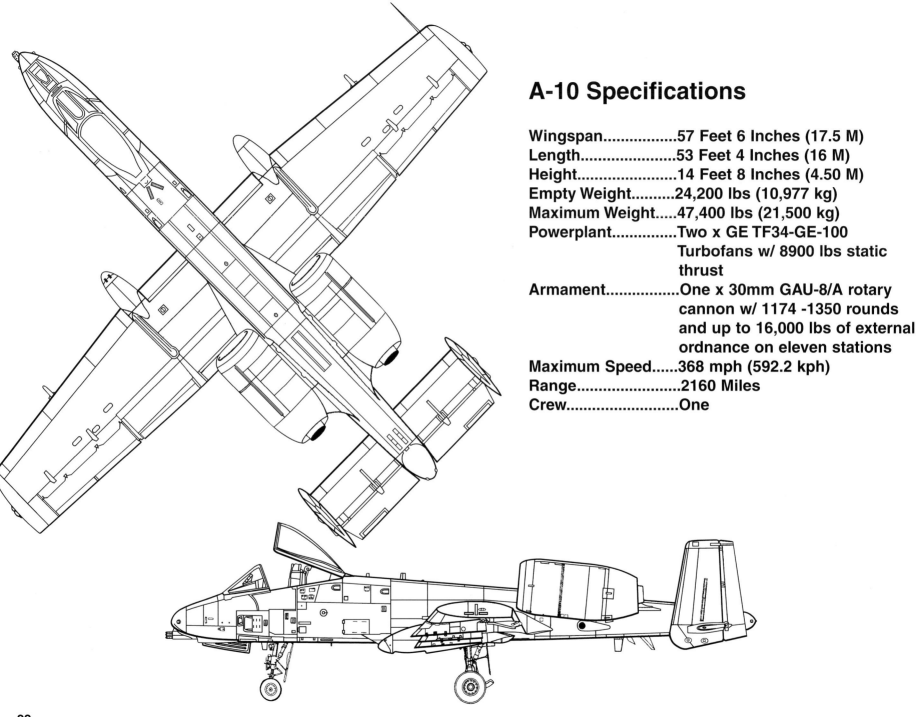

A-10 Specifications

Wingspan.................57 Feet 6 Inches (17.5 M)
Length.....................53 Feet 4 Inches (16 M)
Height......................14 Feet 8 Inches (4.50 M)
Empty Weight..........24,200 lbs (10,977 kg)
Maximum Weight.....47,400 lbs (21,500 kg)
Powerplant...............Two x GE TF34-GE-100
                        Turbofans w/ 8900 lbs static
                        thrust
Armament.................One x 30mm GAU-8/A rotary
                        cannon w/ 1174 -1350 rounds
                        and up to 16,000 lbs of external
                        ordnance on eleven stations
Maximum Speed......368 mph (592.2 kph)
Range........................2160 Miles
Crew...........................One

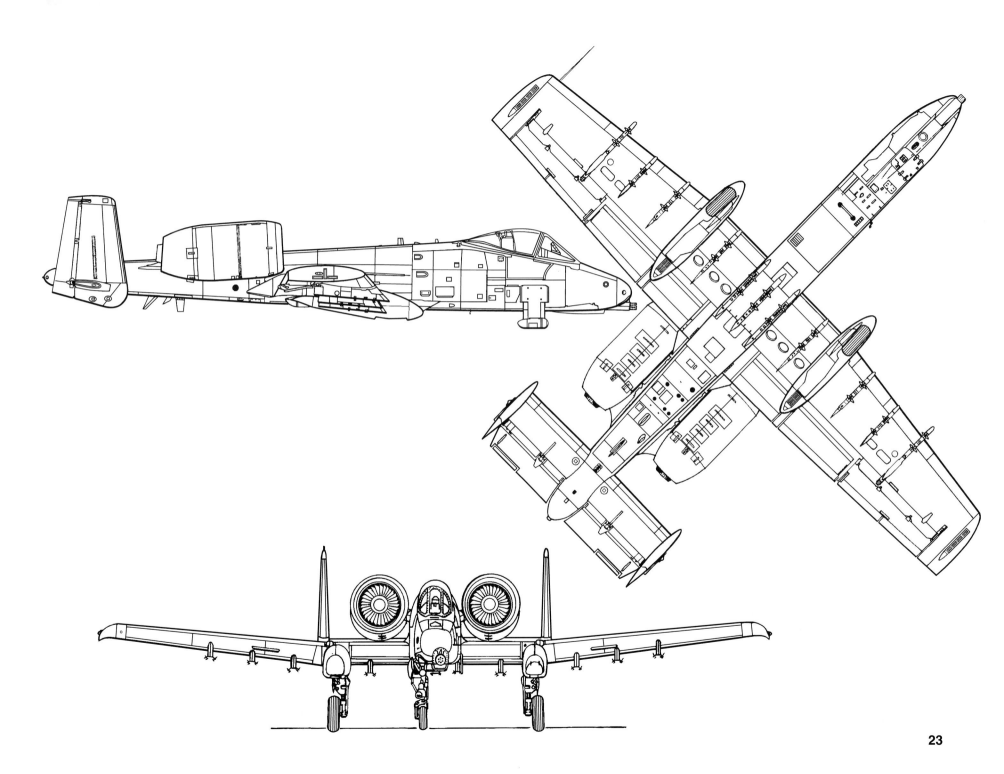

(Above) An AAS-35 PAVE PENNY laser seeking pod hangs off a dedicated pylon on the lower starboard side of the forward fuselage. The pod is used to find targets that have been designated by another laser — whether on the ground or mounted in another aircraft. The cockpit heads-up display (HUD) then displays the laser aiming point to the pilot. The pilot uses this aiming cue to launch his own laser-guided weapons. A clear cap covers the front of the PAVE PENNY pod. Behind the cap is the green seeker element. (Ken Neubeck)

(Left) Perhaps the most distinctive markings painted on A-10s were those used by the 23rd TFW 'Flying Tigers' at England AFB. Louisiana. The unique tiger mouth artwork on the aircraft nose goes back to the days when the unit performed outstanding combat service in China — originally as the American Volunteer Group — during World War II. Two squadrons of the 23rd TFW served with distinction during OPERATION DESERT STORM in early 1991. England AFB was closed in 1992 due to US defense cutbacks. This A-10 lacks the AAS-35 PAVE PENNY pod, however its associated pylon remains in place on the starboard side of the forward fuselage. (Ken Kubik)

The A-10 is equipped with a built-in pilot boarding ladder. The ladder consists of tele-scoping metal sections, each equipped with foot rungs. The ladder negates the require-ment for specialized ladders at other air bases. This is the early version of the ladder with square telescoping sections. (R. Leonard)

The bay is covered by a single access door. The telescoping sections automatically extend when the door is opened, but are manually pushed up and into the stowage bay. Stickers on inside of the ladder access door show some of the stops that this aircraft has made along the way. This is a later production version of the ladder with round telescop-ing tubing. (Ken Kubik)

(Above) The AAS-35 laser seeker pod is slung under its fuselage mounted pylon much like wing ordnance. A-10s routinely fly with or without the PAVE PENNY pod in place. When attached, the pod is rigidly mounted in place — there is no provision for jettisoning the pod in an emergency. (C. Reed)

(Left) A streamlined pylon is bolted to the starboard fuselage side adjacent to the nose gear well to hold the AAS-35 PAVE PENNY laser seeker pod. The pylon is normally a permanent fixture of the A-10, however, the PAVE PENNY pod is is easily removed. (C. Knowles)

(Above) Access to the ladder bay is gained via a switch located aft of the access door immediately to the right of the ladder bay. The inner face of the pilot boarding ladder access door is a popular easel for artwork by the ground crews. The interior of the bay is normally painted light gray.

Pilot Boarding Ladder Switch

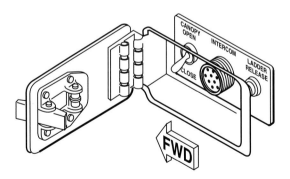

(Right) *Little Darlin* and a Betty Boop cartoon are painted on the inside of the ladder bay access door. Both the door and ladder are spring loaded to open and extend when the access switch is activated. Ground crews must manually retract the ladder and close the door. The ladder housing and foot steps are painted yellow, while the upper surfaces of the steps are given a non-skid black coating. The telescoping sections are an unpainted, dark bare metal color. (C. Knowles)

27

An elbow-shaped arm raises and lowers the aft hinging canopy. The canopy can be operated from inside or outside the aircraft and be completely jettisoned if necessary. The interior canopy frames are painted black to reduce glare. This particular aircraft is on display at the Cradle of Aviation Museum located on Mitchel Field, Long Island, New York. (Ken Neubeck)

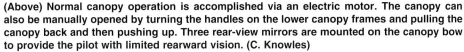

(Above) Normal canopy operation is accomplished via an electric motor. The canopy can also be manually opened by turning the handles on the lower canopy frames and pulling the canopy back and then pushing up. Three rear-view mirrors are mounted on the canopy bow to provide the pilot with limited rearward vision. (C. Knowles)

(Above Right) The canopy hinges downward and then slides forward to form a tight seal against the forward canopy frame. The A-10 can be taxied at a speed of up to 50 knots with the canopy open. Canopies are often left open on hot days to prevent heat build-up within the cockpit. (M. Leay)

(Right) The area behind the seat is relatively featureless and broken only by the canopy raising and lowering mechanism. Air lines at the upper left lead to the canopy defogging system. The circular hoops hold a rarely used thermos bottle. This area is normally painted black. (Ken Kubik)

(Above) Engine and Auxiliary Power Unit (APU) fire extinguisher pull handles are mounted across the top of the main instrument panel. The center handle is for the APU. At the lower corners of the instrument panel are the EMERGENCY BRAKE (left) and the CANOPY JETT(ison) (right) handles. The canopy jettison handle is for emergency use on the ground. (Fairchild Republic Archives)

(Left) The A-10 cockpit layout is fairly standard and most of the flying and engine displays are standard analog dial-type instruments. The Heads Up Display (HUD) is located on the top of the main panel and it is flanked by an accelerometer (left) and a standby compass (right). The primary flying instruments are spread across the top half of the interment panel and down the center section. The weapons control panel is located at the lower left, while the engine instruments are grouped together at the lower right. The darkened TV monitor at the upper right section of the panel is used for target acquisition and guiding the AGM-65 Maverick air-to-ground missile. (Fairchild Republic Archives)

(Below) The throttle quadrant is located at the front of the left console. Behind the throttle quadrant are the panels for controlling the various radios and navigation aids used in the A-10. These panels are modular and easily altered when new electronic systems are introduced into the aircraft. The overall color of the cockpit is light gray with a black instrument panel and consoles. (Fairchild Republic Archives)

(Above) The left console is dominated by the engine throttle quadrant. Immediately in front of the quadrant is a panel containing a series of emergency switches for controlling trim, speed brakes, and weapons. At far right is the landing gear actuation handle. (Fairchild Republic Archives)

(Right) The red trigger at the front of the stick fires the 30mm cannon and activates the gun camera. The buttons on the top operate the trim controls (background) and release weapons (foreground). The angled button on the left side controls missile tracking or the air refueling disconnect, while the horizontal button activates the nosewheel steering or certain HUD and navigation functions. (Fairchild Republic Archives)

(Below) The right console contains the flight data stowage bin for storing maps and other paperwork. The lighting control panel is forward of the bin. This panel controls both internal and external aircraft lighting. The black cylindrical object is a portable cockpit lamp. (Fairchild Republic Archives)

31

Gray sheet metal and modular black instrument clusters neatly hide the maze of wiring and piping in the cockpit. The two yellow grips are the ejection handles for the Advanced Concept Ejection Seat (ACES) II ejection seat. The ACES II is also used in the F-15 Eagle and F-16 Fighting Falcon fighters. (Ken Kubik)

The windscreen quarter panels are resistant to impacts from birds and machine gun rounds, while the front windscreen is bullet proof. The pilot's Heads Up Display (HUD) looks directly through the front windscreen and provides both navigation and weapons aiming cues. (R. Van Dorst)

The A-10 is equipped with the ACES II (Advanced Concept Ejection Seat) seat — the same seat that is used in the USAF F-15 and F-16 supersonic fighters. The apple green oxygen bottle provides oxygen to the pilot during high altitude ejections and can also be used in the cockpit in the event the main oxygen system becomes inoperative. (R. Van Dorst)

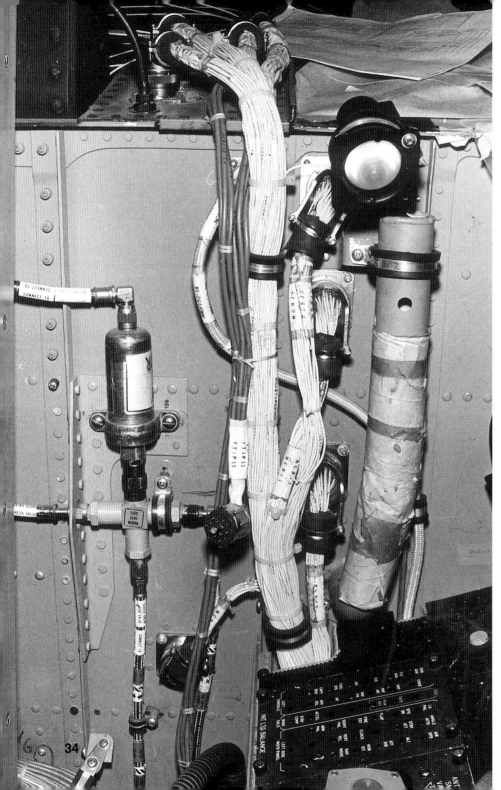

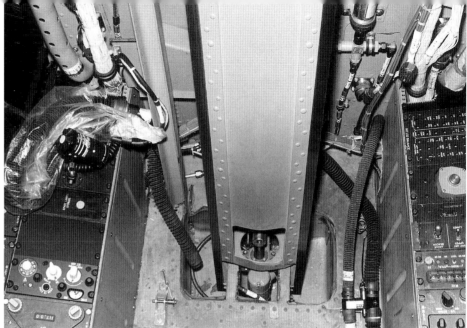

(Above) Removal of the ejection seat reveals the seat rail. When the ejection sequence is initiated, the canopy is jettisoned and the seat rides up the rails. The seat can also break through the canopy in the event the canopy does not separate from the aircraft. The corrugated hoses are fittings for the pilot's oxygen mask and g-suit. (Fairchild Republic Archives)

(Left) The left side of the aft cockpit bulkhead contains additional wiring bundles and the service air lines for the pilot's g-suit. A small cockpit lamp is also mounted on the bulkhead. (Fairchild Republic Archives)

(Below) The A-10's operating environment meant the aircraft would be subject to various forms of anti-aircraft defenses ranging from guns to missiles. A titanium armor 'bathtub' protected the pilot and critical control elements from hostile fire. This armored tub has been assembled and rests on the factory floor at Fairchild Republic. (Fairchild Republic Archives)

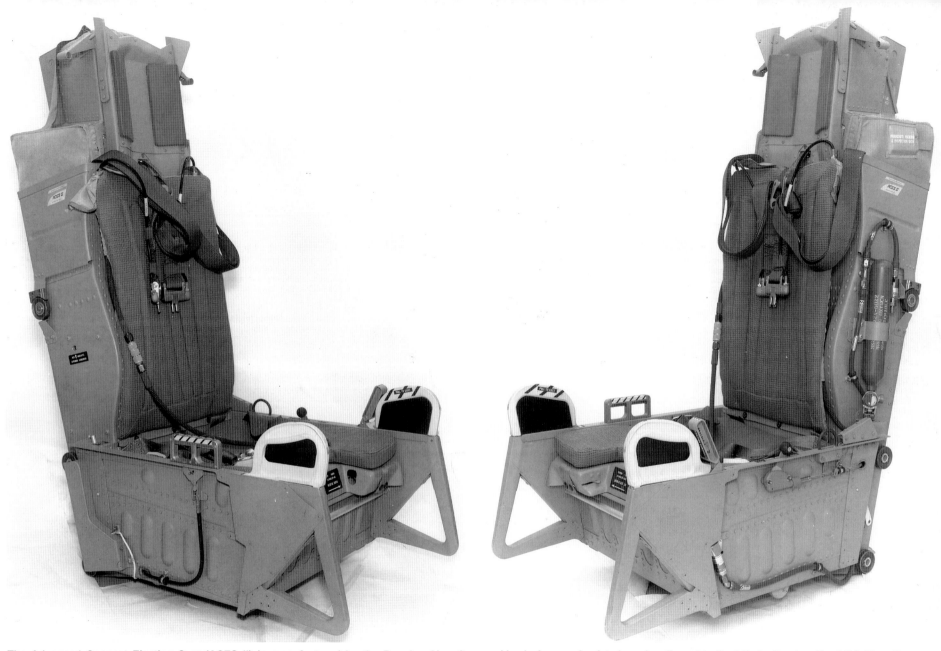

The Advanced Concept Ejection Seat (ACES II) is manufactured by the Douglas Aircraft Corporation and was designed to be used in a variety of USAF tactical aircraft including the F-15 Eagle and the F-16 Fighting Falcon. The ACES II seat is a self-contained unit incorporating a seat bucket with a survival kit, a seat back, and the headrest. The pilot's parachute is incorporated into the seat along with an emergency oxygen supply for high-altitude ejections. Ejection is initiated by pulling one or both yellow handles at the front of the seat up and back. A ground safety lever is adjacent to the left ejection handle. A third handle, located on the right side, is used to release the pilot restraints. The survival kit built into the seat contains a life raft, survival equipment and a radio beacon transmitter which is automatically activated on ejection. The seat is normally painted overall Dark Gull Gray (FS 36231) with khaki belts and cushions, and an apple green (approximately FS 14187) oxygen bottle. (Fairchild Republic Archives)

35

(Above) This A-10 has been fitted with an additional upgrade — a Global Positioning System (GPS) antenna housed within a small circular fairing on the fuselage spine behind the canopy. This system, part of the effort to improve all-weather, night attack capabilities, has not been installed on all A-10s. One of the USAF's new McDonnell-Douglas C-17 Globemaster III transports is parked in the background. (R. Van Dorst)

(Left) The aircraft spine houses small vents to purge cooling air from the aft avionics bays as well as a UHF/TACAN antenna (foreground) and an IFF antenna. Just in front of the IFF antenna are V-shaped night formation strip lights — sometimes referred to as 'slime lights' due to their bright yellow-green color when lit. These were part of an upgrade to improve the A-10's all-weather flying and attack capabilities. (R. Van Dorst)

ACES II Ejection Seat

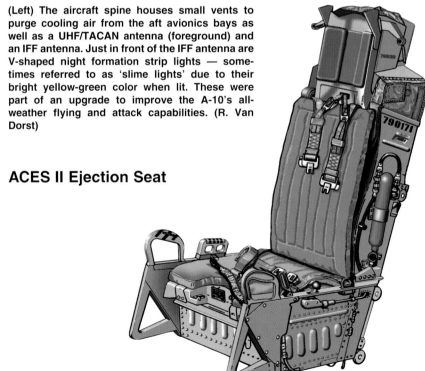

(Above) The port fuselage side houses a small angle of attack vane just in front of the white kill markings. This A-10, Val's Avenger (78-664), was one of the Night Hogs from the 355th TFS — a unit that specialized in night attacks using AGM 65D Maverick missiles during the 1991 Gulf War. The 355th TFS used white target silhouettes with a small black number painted inside to represent ground kills. (Ken Kubik)

(Right) The aircraft spine houses (from the foreground) an engine nacelle floodlight/formation light, two vent tubes, the UHF/TACAN antenna, a GPS antenna dome, an IFF antenna, and V-shaped formation strip lights. The area beneath the nacelle light and TACAN antenna houses the forward main fuselage fuel tank. (R. Van Dorst)

(Below) One of the regularly used access panels is the one used to service the circuit breaker box and electrical buses. This panel is located on the right side just behind the cockpit and beneath the USAF insignia. Most of the A-10's access panels and fuselage skins are flat or have only a single curve — a design feature which eases manufacture and battle damage repair. (Ken Neubeck)

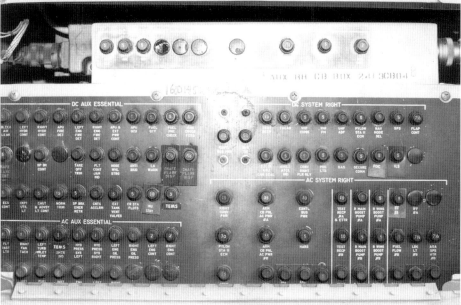

(Above) The starboard side circuit breaker box has the breakers for both the main and auxiliary AC and DC power systems. (Ken Neubeck)

(Left) Opening the circuit breaker bay access door reveals the interior of the DC power system. At the bottom is the right hand circuit breaker box with an electrical bus (a route for power or data) immediately above. Immediately above these components is a cylindrical black solid state converter. The converter handles incoming aircraft power at 100 amps and 28 Volts DC and supplies the power to the various electrical systems throughout the airframe. The remainder of the components in this area are buses, relays, and associated wiring. (Ken Kubik)

(Below) A fiberglass ventral strake is mounted on each side of the lower fuselage in front of the wing. The strakes improve the flow of air around the wing roots and the three center fuselage weapons stations and through the inboard leading edge slats. (Ken Neubeck)

The cooling system intake and exhaust box is nestled between the engine nacelles. The cooling system intake and exhaust box is part of the environmental control system (ECS) which provides conditioned air and pressurization to the cockpit. (R. Van Dorst)

An inboard leading edge slat is located on each wing between the fuselage and main landing gear pod. (Ken Neubeck)

In addition to cockpit air conditioning and pressurization, the ECS furnishes air for windshield and canopy defogging, windshield rain removal, the pilot's g-suit, the canopy seal, the fuel system purge, and external drop tank pressurization. (R. Leonard)

The leading edge slat is powered by two hydraulic rams. The slat is designed to maintain a smooth flow of air over the upper surface of the wing and into the engine at high angles of attack. (C. Knowles)

The A-10 wing consists of three sections: a flat center section and two outer panels with a seven degree dihedral. The center section houses the inboard flap segments and the landing gear pods. The outer wing panel houses the outboard flap section, the aileron/speed brakes (also referred to as decelerons), and three weapons pylons. (R. Van Dorst)

Both the aileron and its trim tab incorporate mass balances into their lower surfaces. The aileron actuating ram protrudes from the trailing edge of the outermost wing pylon. (C. Knowles)

The ailerons are used to control roll and both are equipped with trim tabs controlled by a solid actuating rod. (R. Van Dorst)

The ailerons are actuated by a single hydraulic ram mounted in the after root section of the outermost weapons pylons. (R. Van Dorst)

The A-10 is equipped with split ailerons which can be used as speed brakes both in the air and on the ground. This A-10 had just completed a demonstration flight for members of the Iranian Air Force at Eglin AFB, Florida and was returning to Long Island. Despite the best efforts of Fairchild-Republic, there were no export orders for the A-10. (Fairchild Republic Archives)

The A-10 can roll-out in approximately 1300 feet with flaps down and the speed brakes extended. The aircraft is not equipped with a braking parachute. The speed brake interiors on the initial test aircraft were painted red, however operational A-10s have the inner faces of the brakes painted Dark Gray (FS 36081) or Dark Ghost Gray (FS36320) depending on the exterior scheme. (Fairchild Republic Archives)

Each wing is equipped with a pair of trailing edge Fowler flaps — one on the center section and one on the outer wing panel. Full flap deflection for landing is limited to 20°. The flaps are set to 7° for take-off and maneuvering, but will automatically retract when the airspeed exceeds 185 - 210 knots. (R. Van Dorst)

Each flap section is actuated by a single hydraulic ram. The flaps slide aft, increasing the wing chord, and then drop downward to increase the wing camber. Both actions provide additional lift at low speeds for take off, combat maneuvering, and landing. (R. Van Dorst)

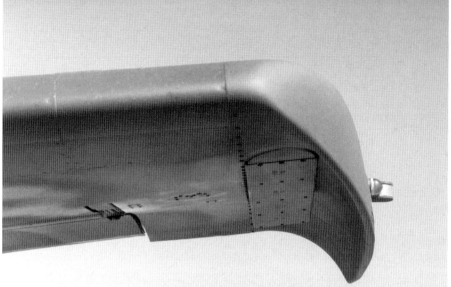

(Above) The downturn of the fiberglass-epoxy wing tip improves the flow of air over the ailerons. The tip also incorporates the position lights (red to port, blue-green to starboard) and a white strobe light. The rectangular fairing under the wing tip is a base for an ALE-40 chaff/flare dispenser. (Pete Nelson)

(Left) The trailing edge flaps slide along a pair of tracks to prevent skewing which could alter aircraft trim and provide unwanted control changes. This is especially important in combat when these changes could cause the aircraft to pull off a target.

(Below) ALE-40 Chaff/Flare Dispensers are mounted under both wing tips. The base of the dispenser has been covered over by a flat plate. The sharp trailing edge of the wing becomes blunter and rounder at the wing tip. (C. Reed)

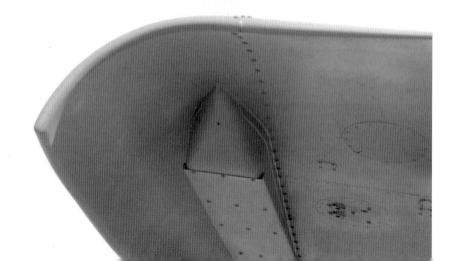

The starboard wing tip houses a blue-green position light and a flashing white strobe light. During the late 1980s, a Low Altitude Safety and Targeting Enhancement (LASTE) program was begun which greatly improved the Warthog's attack and night/all-weather flying capabilities. The upside-down T-shaped formation strip lights were added as a result of the LASTE program. (C. Knowles)

The tip of the pitot tube is heated to prevent icing. The unpainted tip gradually takes on a burnt metal appearance., however, the remainder of the tube retains its camouflage.

The starboard wing tip also serves as the mount for the pitot tube which serves as a conduit for air used to measure the A-10's airspeed. The formation strip lights on the wing tip have a milky yellow color when off, but glow a bright yellow-green when activated. (R. Van Dorst)

Weapon station number nine is mounted just outboard of the starboard main gear pod. Weapon stations numbers three (on the port wing) and nine can each carry up to three AGM-65 Maverick missiles. A small stall strip is installed on each wing leading edge. (Ken Neubeck)

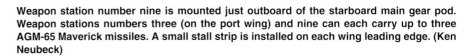

Flaps down and speed brakes open, an Alaskan-based A-10 floats in ground effect (a cushion of air compressed between the aircraft and the ground) just prior to touch down on a rain slicked runway. The A-10 is equipped with an anti-skid braking system on both main wheels to prevent the aircraft from suddenly diverging off the runway due to uneven braking. This A-10 was one of seven Warthogs assigned to the 11th Tactical Air Support Squadron, 343rd Wing during the early 1990s. Both the 11th TASS and the 343rd Wing were inactivated during the late summer of 1993 and replaced by the 355th Fighter Squadron and the 354th Fighter Wing. (A. Antonivk)

The A-10 is equipped with two fully retracting, but not fully enclosed, single wheel main gear units. The gear struts are normally painted Aircraft Gray (FS 16473), however, white struts have also been seen on some aircraft.

Thirty-six inch, circumferential tread Goodyear tires are used on both main wheels. Hydraulic brakes, actuated via the rudder pedals, are mounted on each inner wheel hub. The A-10 is also equipped with an emergency brake handle.

Torque links are placed fore-and-aft on the oleo shock absorber. The aft torque link is covered with a small fairing which joins up with vertical fairing attached to the rear of the main gear strut. (R. Leonard)

Two retracting rods hold the single strut door to the main gear strut. The main gear doors cover the strut and retracting rod, but leave the wheel and tire exposed. (R. Van Dorst)

Hydraulic lines snake down the front of the main gear strut to their attachment points around the brake mechanism. (R. Van Dorst)

(Above) A single hydraulic ram raises and lowers the main gear. The strut door is hinged at the top and pulled closed when the gear is retracted into the well. (Dennis R. Jenkins)

(Left) The forward retracting main gear was semi-enclosed into pods mounted on the wings. Landing gear retraction and extension was accomplished using hydraulic power. The landing gear can be extended by using gravity in an emergency. Weapon station number 8, to the right of the landing gear pod, carries a triple ejector rack and three BDU-33 practice bombs. (Ken Kubik)

(Below) All three main gear doors are attached to the strut via retracting rods or clamps. Only the tire and a small portion of the wheel remain exposed to the slipstream. (Dennis R. Jenkins)

The forged main gear struts are hinged at the rear of the shallow strut well. The strut wells are normally painted Aircraft Gray (FS 16473). (R. Van Dorst)

The aft section of the starboard main gear pod is similar to that of the port gear pod. The interiors of the gear pods suffer from the effects of maintenance and being partially exposed to the elements. Dirt, stains, and paint touch-ups are common. (R. Van Dorst)

The front half of the main gear pod is deeper in order to accommodate the main wheel and tire. This is the wheel well in the port main gear pod. The black pipe leads to the single-point pressure refueling receptacle in the front of the pod. (R. Van Dorst)

The forward section of the starboard main gear pod lacks the fuel pipe found in the port pod, but is otherwise similar in construction and fitting. (R. Van Dorst)

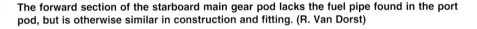

47

The roof of the starboard main gear pod is relatively uncluttered to provide clearance for the wheel and tire. (C. Knowles)

The interior of the port main gear pod is similar to that of the starboard pod except for the fuel pipe leading to the single-point ground pressure refueling receptacle. (C. Knowles)

(Above) A wing fence is installed just inboard of each main landing gear pod. The fence improves the air flow around the inner face of the pod and through the slat. (Ken Neubeck)

(Above Right) The front of the port main gear pod opens up to expose the nozzle fitting and control panel for the single-point pressure refueling system. Both wing and fuselage fuel tanks, as well as any external tanks, can be refueled from this one point. The wing and fuselage tanks are also equipped with their own filling points on the upper wing surfaces and fuselage spine respectively. (R. Van Dorst)

(Right) The refueling system access door is opened by depressing two quick release latches on top of the pod. The open door reveals the refueling receptacle on the left and the fuel system control panel box on the right. Opening the door activates a microswitch — a small rod visible between the two upper latches — which activates the system. (Ken Neubeck)

49

(Above) The after section of both landing gear pods is equipped with a set of ALE-40 Chaff/Flare dispensers to supplement those mounted under the wing tips. The boxes and rear faring can be removed and the opening closed off with a cover plate. (C. Knowles)

Single Point Refueling System

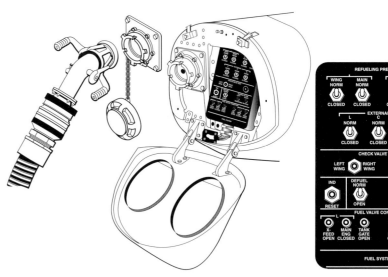

(Left) A fuel nozzle is attached to the receptacle during a ground refueling operation. This is a single point refueling port — all of the A-10's fuel cells can be refueled from this receptacle. A ground wire, used to prevent static electric discharges, is plugged into the grounding point just behind the open panel. (Ken Kubik)

The A-10 Thunderbolt II is powered by a pair of TF-34 high bypass ratio turbofan engines developed by the General Electric Company of Binghamton, New York. The fan blades are on the left side of the engine in this photo, with the compressor section in the middle, and the exhaust turbines on the right. These engines are quieter in comparison to conventional jet engines — a feature that often allows the aircraft to mask its approach using battlefield noise. (Fairchild Republic Archives)

Accessory units attached to the engines provide power to operate electrical and hydraulic systems in the A-10. Many of these accessories are redundant, with each engine driving its own accessories. Consequently the loss of one engine in combat does not mean the complete loss of any one utility system. Each factory fuselage and wing set was accompanied by a pair of engines shipped in their own containers. (Ken Neubeck)

An engine technician repairs an oil leak on an A-10's port TF-34 engine which had been damaged by Iraqi ground fire. The engine mount's trailing edge fairing has also been removed. (Fred Schlenker III)

The open face of the TF-34 engine reveals the first stage fan blades. Air is pulled into the engine and progressively compressed through several stages before being mixed with fuel and burned. (R. Van Dorst)

The after section of the engine reveals the engine exhaust nozzle in the center. The open area around the nozzle is the bypass air outlet — not all of the air pulled into the front of engine is burned. Approximately 85% of the engines' thrust is provided by the bypass air. Additionally, the cooler bypass air mixes with the hotter exhaust to lower the infra-red (IR) signature. This serves to inhibit the ability of IR missiles to track the A-10. (R. Van Dorst)

(Above) Both engines are attached to the aft fuselage using an airfoil shaped pylon. The aft fuselage section also contains the Environmental Control System (ECS) cooling box (between the engines), and the Auxiliary Power Unit (APU) (inside the fuselage below the engine pylons). (C. Knowles)

(Below) An A-10 of the 355th Tactical Fighter Squadron taxis in from a long flight from the Middle East after taking part in OPERATION DESERT STORM. The aircraft is carrying a pair of 600 gallon ferry tanks inboard of the landing gear pods, a centerline baggage pod, and an ALQ-119 Electronic Counter measures (ECM) Pod on weapons station 11. (Fred Schlenker III)

(Above) An early production A-10 tucks its gear up while making a low pass during an air show at Myrtle Beach AFB, South Carolina. The USAF began to revert to the earlier two-tone gray scheme for the A-10 during the early 1990s. (Fairchild Republic Archives)

Beneath the port engine pod is a small drain pipe enshrouded by an airfoil shaped fairing. The exhaust outlet for the Auxiliary Power Unit (APU) is placed on the port side of the fuselage just below the engine pod. (R. Van Dorst)

The APU exhaust is surrounded by a teardrop-shaped reinforcing plate. This exhaust has a small baffle added to direct the exhaust down and aft of the engine pod. The port fuselage and lower engine cowling are often heavily stained from the APU exhaust. (R. Van Dorst)

The starboard side of the aft fuselage reveals the APU inlet. The APU is a small turbine engine designed to provide electric and hydraulic power for the aircraft systems when the engines are not running or a ground power cart is not available. The APU uses jet fuel. (R. Van Dorst)

Quick release latches close down the engine's clamshell maintenance access doors. Almost the entire cowl can be opened up which allows easy and rapid access to the engines. The fairing encloses a drain tube for the aft section of the engine pod. (Ken Neubeck)

54

CAUTION-CHECK SHROUD DOOR LATCHES TO
ASSURE THAT THE LATCHES ARE ENGAGED AND
LOCKED PRIOR TO CLOSING THE NACELLE DOORS

The underside of the aft fuselage section is composed of several maintenance access panels. These panels have had their quick-turn fasteners released which pops them out of the panel.

The hydraulic system service points have their own small door set into one of the larger lower aft fuselage doors. Instructions for routine servicing are conveniently placed on the inner face of the door. Retaining chains for each cap prevents their loss on the flightline.

The Auxiliary Power Unit (APU) and hydraulic system service points are accessed through the doors in the lower part of the aft fuselage. (Ken Kubik)

The hydraulic system is designed to be filled under pressure from below — a faster operation than simply pouring hydraulic fluid into a reservoir. (Ken Neubeck)

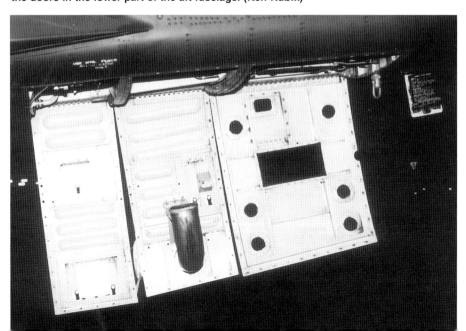

The wing roots are neatly faired into the fuselage using formed metal panels. Keeping the air smoothly flowing around this area is important. The engines require an uninterrupted flow of air at all maneuvering angles to maintain the high thrust needed for combat. (R. Van Dorst)

The round head rivets are used throughout much of the aft fuselage in standard rectangular patterns. The A-10 was designed to engage massed Warsaw Pact tank formations at close quarters, consequently, it was expected to be hit. The simple construction methods, redundant systems, and in some cases interchangeable parts, made the A-10 relatively easy to manufacture, hard to kill, and simple to repair. (Ken Neubeck)

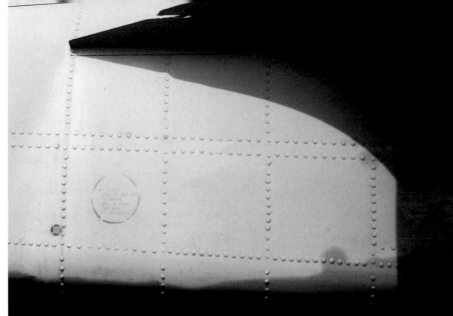

The lower aft fuselage is another area where antennas begin to sprout from the fuselage. The aft fuselage is covered with exposed, round head rivets versus the flush rivets used on the forward fuselage section. (R. Van Dorst)

The extensive use of non-flush riveting on the A-10 airframe is a throwback to some of the assembly techniques used in World War II — mainly on tanks. (Ken Neubeck)

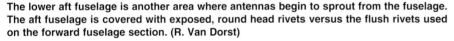

The tail cone houses a dual-purpose white position and white strobe anti-collision light. This A-10 lacks the two ALR-69 Radar Warning Receiver antennas that are normally flanking the light. The tail cone inscription reads FOLLOW ME TO KUWAIT.

The A-10's horizontal stabilizer is built as a single unit and then attached to the lower aft fuselage. The elevators are interchangeable from port to starboard. Each elevator is operated using a single hydraulic ram. The ram and elevators are interconnected to allow both elevators to function using a single ram. (C. Knowles)

The low mounted horizontal stabilizer and elevators and the twin vertical fins provide a degree of control redundancy in the event that one of the elevators or vertical fins is lost due to damage. Additionally both the stabilizer and vertical fins serve to mask the hottest portion of the exhaust plume from heat-seeking missiles. (R. Van Dorst)

On the other hand, if an enemy can not hit the engines, sometimes the tail is the next best thing... . Col David A. Sawyer, the commander of the 23rd TFW, was hit by an Iraqi Surface-to-Air Missile (SAM). The missile blew off the tail cone, shredded the starboard elevator, and holed both vertical fins and rudders. Col Sawyer maintained control and brought the damaged A-10 back to King Fahd IAP, Saudi Arabia. Eighteen A-10s received major hits during DESERT STORM and six of these A-10s were destroyed. (USAF)

The lower aft fuselage houses (L to R) the VHF/FM antenna, a fuel dump pipe, and the VHF/AM antenna. Both antennas are on the aircraft centerline, while the fuel dump pipe is offset to port. The open door covers the external air receptacle which is used in conjunction with a ground air cart when engine bleed air is not available.

Each elevator is equipped with an outboard rod actuated trim tab. A narrow fairing covers the rod.

Quick release latches hold the hinged tail cone to the aft fuselage. Opening the tail cone provides access to the white position/strobe light and both ALR-69 RWR antennas. (Ken Neubeck)

A white position/anti-collision strobe light is mounted in the extreme tip of the tail cone. This aircraft is missing the two ALR-69 RWR antennas normally mounted on either side of the strobe light. The black cover below the strobe light is another radar warning receiver antenna. This antenna cover was seen less frequently on later production aircraft. (Ken Neubeck)

(Above) The rudder actuator is covered by a single-piece, formed sheet metal fairing. The fairing extends back the vertical fin trailing edge, but leaves the remainder of the rod and the rudder linkage exposed.

(Right) A-10s were later modified as part of the LASTE (Low-Altitude Safety and Targeting Enhancement) upgrade program. The two raised blisters at the bottom of the fin are radar altimeter antennas that were added to several A-10s after DESERT STORM. (Ken Kubik)

(Below) Removing the fairing over the rudder actuator reveals the hydraulic ram that operates the rudder. This actuator was on the second YA-10. (Fairchild Republic Archives)

This A-10 has not yet received the modifications added during the LASTE upgrade program. In some respects, the fin and rudder assembly are no more sophisticated than that of a WW II B-25 bomber. This A-10 is assigned to the 118th Fighter Squadron, 103rd Fighter Group of the Connecticut Air National Guard (CTANG). The 103rd FG was the first ANG unit to receive the A-10. (Ken Kubik)

Another element of the Low-Altitude Safety and Targeting Enhancement program was the addition of formation strip lighting to the A-10. These lights are grafted onto the skin of the vertical fin and sealed with a putty-like material. The front half of the fin is flush riveted, while the rear half uses round head rivets to fasten the skin onto the internal ribs. (C. Knowles)

A solid pushrod and external horn are used to control the rudder. The control horn is surrounded by small access panels and a reinforcing plate. Each of the primary flight controls — ailerons, elevators, and rudders — are equipped with artificial feel devices to simulate aerodynamic loads on the control surfaces. These loads are transmitted back to the pilot's control stick where they provide a sense of resistance to the pilot.

The vertical fin construction is identical on both sides of the fin. The two fins are interchangeable from left to right to ease replacement. The top of the rudder incorporates a mass balance into its leading edge. The balance fits into a slot cut into the trailing edge of the fin. Formation strip lights have been added to the fuselage spine immediately in front of the tail cone. (R. Van Dorst)

A-10s were deployed to a number of forward operating locations in Europe with the main base being the 81st TFW at RAF Bentwaters, UK. This A-10 is in a protective hanger at Bentwaters. (Fairchild Republic Archives)

The A-10 uses two versions of the AGM-65 missile — the AGM-65B (Scene Magnification) and the AGM-65D (Imaging Infra-Red). The AGM-65B, shown here, is used for daylight operations, while the AGM-65D is used primarily at night or in conditions of poor visibility. (Ken Neubeck)

The A-10 is designed to use most of the air-to-ground ordnance within the USAF inventory. The weapon of choice for anti-tank operations is the AGM-65 Maverick missile. This is a training round as evidenced by the lack of fins at the rear of the missile. (C. Reed)

The AGM-65 launch rail is attached to the wing pylon. The missile is then attached to the rail. A clean separation from the rail is required in order for the missile to guide to the target. (Fairchild Republic Archives)

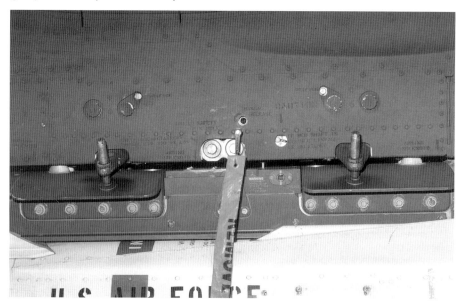

OA-10s serving in the Forward Air Controller role carry white phosphorus rockets in this seven round LAU-68 launcher. The rockets are used for marking targets for other aircraft. OA-10s were the primary aircraft for the USAF forward observer mission during OPERATION DESERT STORM. (Ken Neubeck)

The A-10 often carries a pair of infra-red guided AIM-9 Sidewinder air-to-air missiles for self defense. The missiles are usually mounted in pairs on store station 1 or 11 (the outer wing pylons). (Ken Neubeck)

The A-10 can also carry an assortment of iron bombs and cluster munitions ranging from 250 to 2000 pounds each. This Triple Ejector Rack (TER) can carry three 500 pound bombs on a single store station — usually numbers three and nine just outside the landing gear pods. (Ken Neubeck)

Trunk space was not a design consideration when the A-10 was built. Pilots taking extended trips carry their personal belongings and manuals in this baggage pod. These pods are usually mounted on one of the fuselage pylons.

After a few years of service, it was discovered that gun gases ingested into the A-10's TF-34 engines could cause either an over temperature or flameout condition. A DT&E test aircraft was used to test a rotary pinwheel device attached to the end of the extended gun barrels. Extensive weapons firing has resulted in heavy staining to the front of this aircraft. (Fairchild Republic Archives)

A-10 (79-150) wears the more recent camouflage scheme of two-tone gray — a reversion to the earlier MASK-10 schemes used during the 1970s. Dark gray paint has been used to paint the Warthog nose art and, once again, the forward ALR-69 RWR antenna covers offer a convenient location for the 'Hog's nostrils. (R. Van Dorst)

This A-10, equipped with the latest LASTE modifications, is parked on the ramp under threatening skies at Travis AFB, California in May of 1998. (R. Van Dorst)

The A-10 is deployed both in the continental United States and at bases overseas in Europe and the Pacific. This Alaskan-based A-10, wearing a pristine European I camouflage scheme, was deployed to Osan Air Base, Korea in 1990. (C. Knowles)

Many A-10s revived an earlier tradition during OPERATION DESERT STORM when they were given nose art ranging from small and simple to large and elaborate displays of the artists' skills. This 706th TFS A-10 (S/N 78-582) wears Warthog nose art that is reminiscent of that worn earlier by the unit at Barksdale AFB, Louisiana. This A-10 was named 'Alligator'. (Anthony Abbott)

A-10s also found their way to RAF Alconbury, England in 1987 when the 10th Tactical Reconnaissance Wing (TRW) was redesignated the 10th Tactical Fighter Wing (TFW). The gray tail stripe on this A-10 indicates it was assigned to the 509th TFS. The 10th TFW was also home to the 511th TFS — their aircraft wearing a black fin stripe. (C. Knowles)

This A-10 was assigned to Suwon AB, Korea during the early 1980s. The aircraft is equipped with the pinwheel device over the cannon muzzles. Use of the Battelle Labs device, designed to disperse gun gases, was short-lived when it was found to contribute to airframe fatigue and cracking in the forward fuselage. (C. Knowles)

An A-10 of the 355th TFS, 354th TFW slowly taxis forward while deployed to Nellis AFB, Nevada. The 354th TFW was based at Myrtle Beach, South Carolina, but like all USAF tactical units, routinely deployed to Nellis AFB for their continuing series of Red Flag exercises. (C. Knowles)

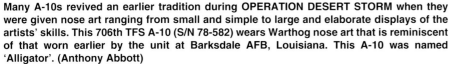

A-10 Primary Antennas, External Lights, and Service Points

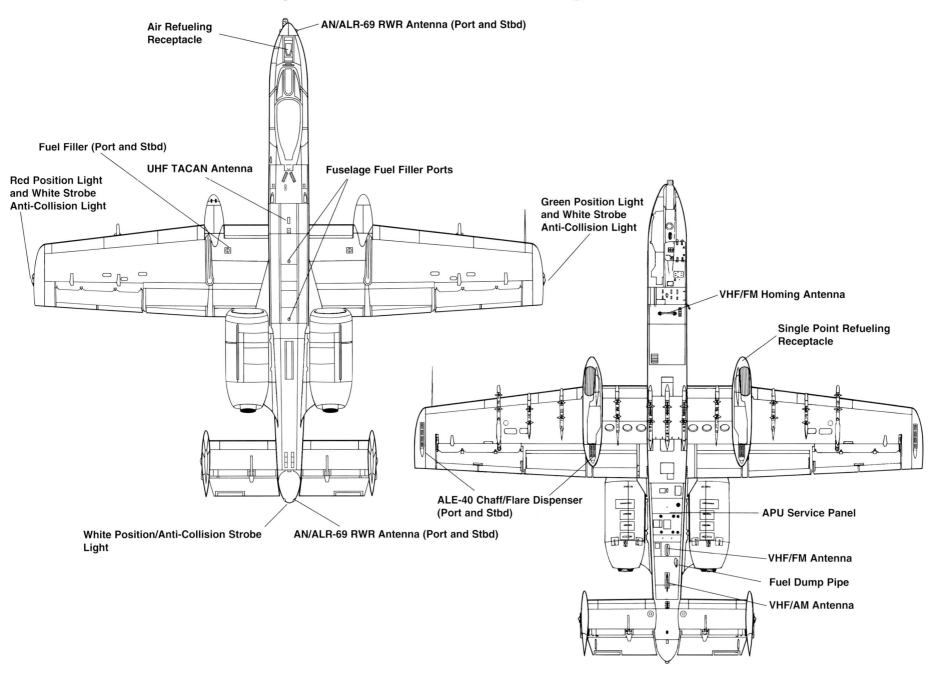

Air Refueling Receptacle

AN/ALR-69 RWR Antenna (Port and Stbd)

Fuel Filler (Port and Stbd)

UHF TACAN Antenna

Fuselage Fuel Filler Ports

Rcd Position Light and White Strobe Anti-Collision Light

Green Position Light and White Strobe Anti-Collision Light

VHF/FM Homing Antenna

Single Point Refueling Receptacle

ALE-40 Chaff/Flare Dispenser (Port and Stbd)

APU Service Panel

White Position/Anti-Collision Strobe Light

AN/ALR-69 RWR Antenna (Port and Stbd)

VHF/FM Antenna

Fuel Dump Pipe

VHF/AM Antenna

Val's Avenger, an A-10 (78-664) assigned to the 355th TFS, awaits repairs to her wing and the starboard engine after being damaged during the Gulf War. (Fred Schlenker III)

Val's Avenger suffered extensive damage to her starboard wing as a result of a missile hit during OPERATION DESERT STORM. Blast and the slipstream have peeled away much of the wing leading edge and upper skin exposing the zinc chromate yellow interior. The blast of the missile warhead severed the first and second wing spars and damaged the third. The damaged third spar and the remaining wing skin were all that were holding the wing together. The wing was quickly removed and replaced by repair crews before the A-10 was returned to action. The pilot of this aircraft, Captain Paul Johnson, received the Air Force Cross for flying this A-10 back to base and for his participation in the rescue of a downed pilot earlier in the war. Triple spars in the wing and horizontal stabilizer greatly contributed to the survivability of the A-10, a trait it shared with one of its ancestors — the Republic P-47 Thunderbolt. (Fred Schlenker III)

The A-10 continues to be tested by several USAF facilities. This A-10 is one of a number of A-10s assigned to Eglin AFB, Florida for weapons delivery testing. The port engine cowling bears the triangular remains of a Sacramento Air Logistics Center (SM-ALC) Decal. The SM-ALC is another USAF agency tasked with testing upgrades to various USAF aircraft. (Daniel Brown)

Eglin AFB, Florida also has this A-10 — wearing the more recent two-tone gray camouflage scheme — on charge. The A-10 is equipped with Triple Ejector Racks on the inboard wing pylons as well as a dual launch rail for the AIM-9 Sidewinder on the starboard outer pylon. (Daniel Brown)

A-10 European One Camouflage Scheme

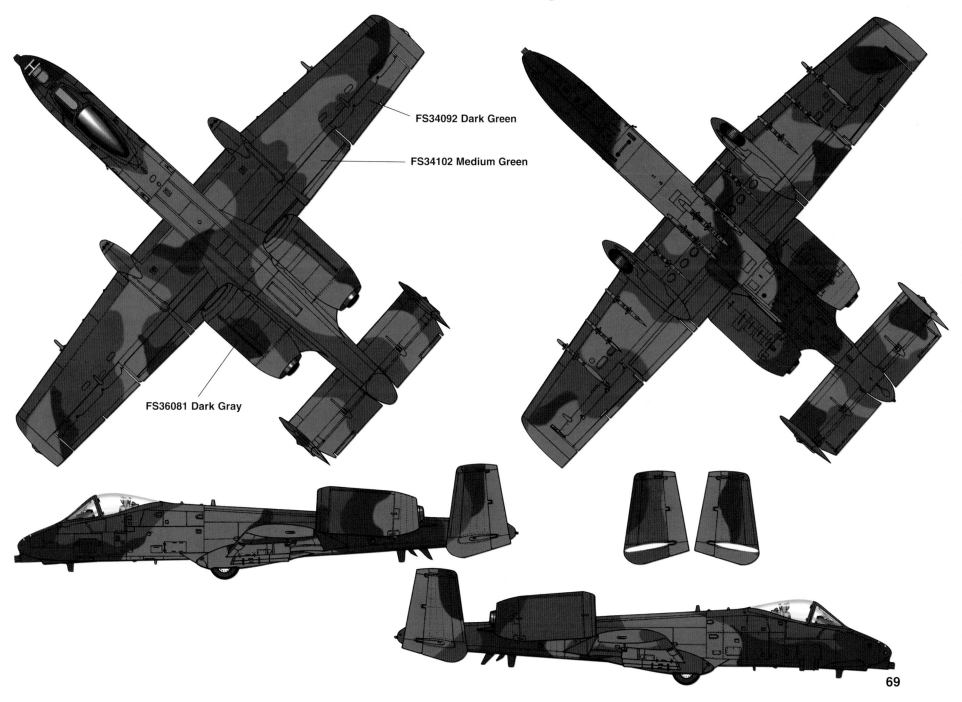

FS34092 Dark Green

FS34102 Medium Green

FS36081 Dark Gray

A large concrete block serves as an anchor during full power engine tests on this A-10. The test box to the right of the nose landing gear is an engine diagnostic display unit. Why the aircraft is fully armed while undergoing engine tests is not known. (Fred Schlenker III)

A-10s of the 906th TFG taxi past their revetments armed with AGM-65 Maverick missiles and what are believed to Mk 7 Rockeye anti-tank cluster bombs prior to a mission during the Gulf War. (Fred Schlenker III)

A-10 (78-622) Fear No Evil from the 355th TFS was the first A-10 to return to base on the first day of the war. Fear No Evil is still carrying her AIM-9L Sidewinder missile on the port outer pylon. (Fred Schlenker III)

A groundcrew member removes the safety pins from an AIM-9 Sidewinder missile. A-10s routinely carried missiles for self-defense, however, none were used against Iraqi aircraft. Both A-10 kills were accomplished using the GAU-8/A cannon. (USAF)

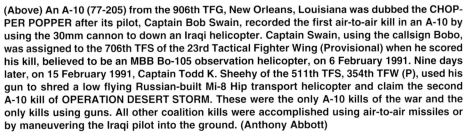

(Above) An A-10 (77-205) from the 906th TFG, New Orleans, Louisiana was dubbed the CHOP-PER POPPER after its pilot, Captain Bob Swain, recorded the first air-to-air kill in an A-10 by using the 30mm cannon to down an Iraqi helicopter. Captain Swain, using the callsign Bobo, was assigned to the 706th TFS of the 23rd Tactical Fighter Wing (Provisional) when he scored his kill, believed to be an MBB Bo-105 observation helicopter, on 6 February 1991. Nine days later, on 15 February 1991, Captain Todd K. Sheehy of the 511th TFS, 354th TFW (P), used his gun to shred a low flying Russian-built Mi-8 Hip transport helicopter and claim the second A-10 kill of OPERATION DESERT STORM. These were the only A-10 kills of the war and the only kills using guns. All other coalition kills were accomplished using air-to-air missiles or by maneuvering the Iraqi pilot into the ground. (Anthony Abbott)

(Above Right) Falcon I of the 355th TFS, Myrtle Beach AFB, SC, arrives home after the end of the Gulf War. The target silhouettes remain painted on the side of the aircraft, however, the tally numbers were removed by order of the unit commander. (Fred Schlenker III)

(Right) The DAWG HAWG (79-097) was flown by Lt Col J Barton of the 355th TFS, Myrtle Beach AFB, SC. (Anthony Abbott)

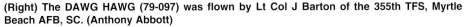

When originally conceived, the A-10 was to wear the old Southeast Asia Scheme of green and tan. When the prototype was rolled out, however, it wore an overall gray scheme with prominent US insignia and black and red markings.

This A-10 assigned to the 355th Tactical Fighter Squadron wears the early operational scheme of two grays — known as MASK — over the upper and lower surfaces.

Operational A-10s were originally camouflaged in the two-tone MASK gray schemes. This A-10 assigned to Davis-Monthan AFB in Arizona was also given a false canopy under the nose. The false canopy was designed to confuse the orientation of the A-10 — banking toward the observer or banking away from the observer.

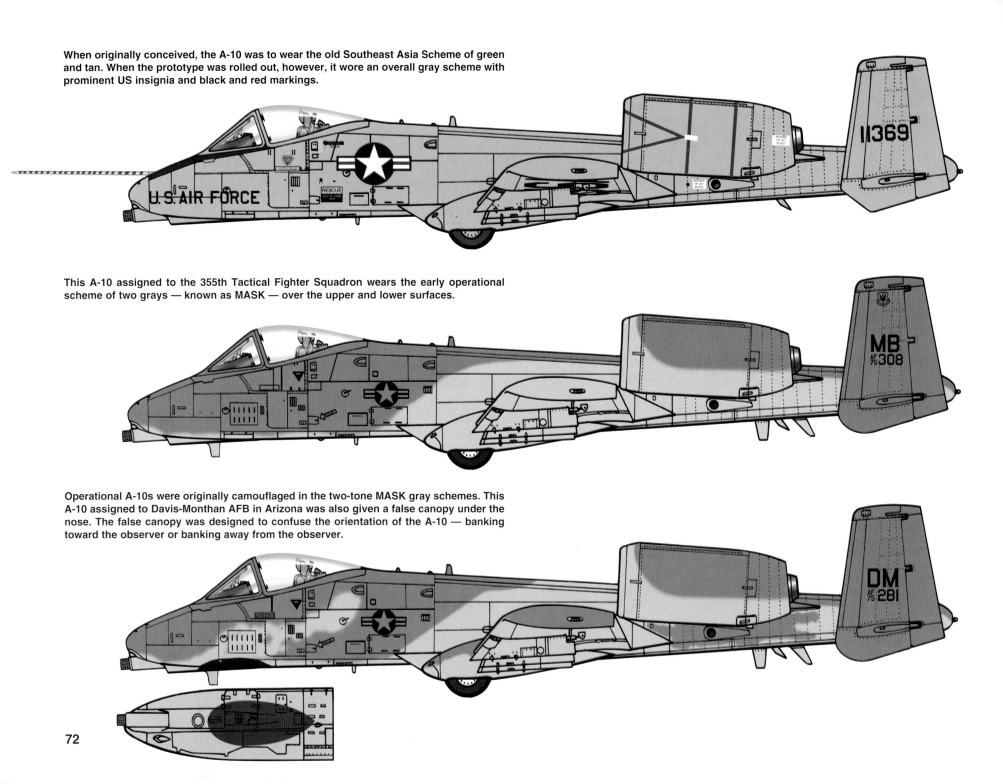

Early in its career, the A-10 was briefly tested with a variety of tan, green, and brown camouflage schemes designed to camouflage the aircraft at low level where the A-10 spent most of its combat time. Collectively, these schemes were known as the JAWS (Joint All-Weather Attack System) schemes. This A-10 was assigned to the 57th Tactical Training Wing.

This A-10, assigned to the 343rd Composite Wing, wore a special black and white winter scheme while taking part in exercises at Kotzebue Air Station in Alaska during 1982.

The 917th Tactical Fighter Wing applied an experimental three-tone gray camouflage scheme to this A-10 in order to improve its protection against the sky or the ground. The scheme, known as 'Flipper', consisted of FS36081 Dark Gray, FS36270 Medium Gray, and FS36375 Light Ghost Gray and was developed in late 1990 for use during OPERATION DESERT STORM. The scheme was ordered removed before the aircraft was committed to action. The return to the European I camouflage scheme during the Gulf War proved to be detrimental to the A-10 since the darker scheme made the aircraft an easier target in the sky.

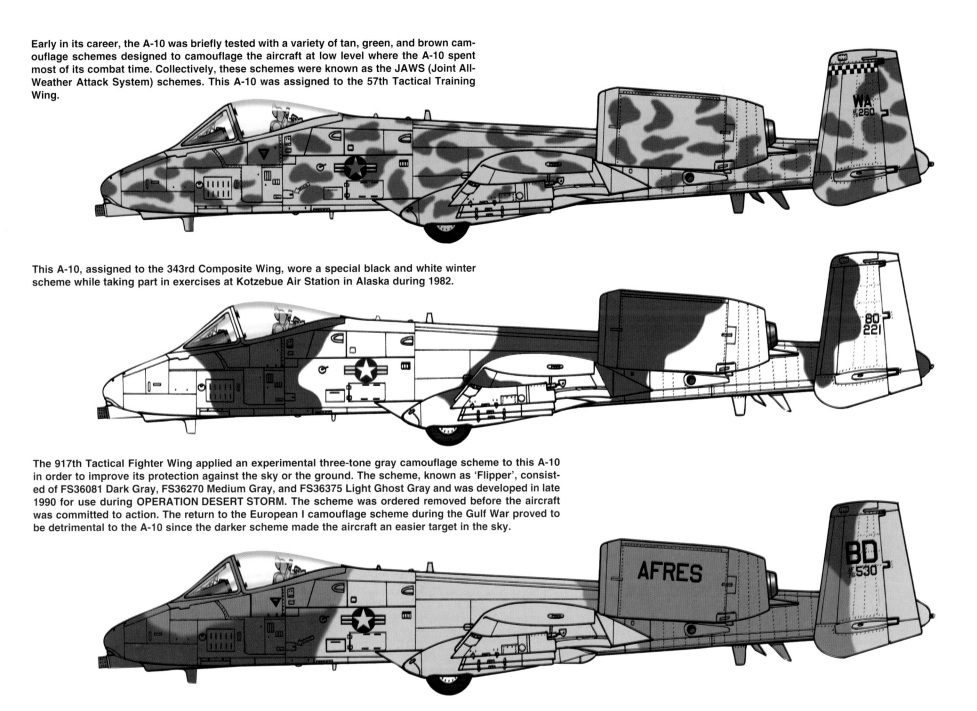

A-10 (78-594), Panther Princess, was assigned to the 353rd TFS 'Panthers'. Her nose art depicts a princess riding a blazing 30mm GAU-8/A cannon. (Anthony Abbott)

Kiss of DEATH, an A-10 (78-677) of the 353rd TFS, Myrtle Beach AFB, SC, had a woman's head blowing a Maverick kiss to Iraqi leader Saddam Hussein. Maverick missiles and blazing guns were a common theme in most A-10 nose art during OPERATION DESERT STORM. (Anthony Abbott)

HOLY *~•••+!, an A-10 (77-271) assigned to the 706th TFS, depicted a camel riding Saddam Hussein being pursued by an 'angry' Maverick missile. Kill markings for this unit were recorded using vertical white slashes painted next to red target silhouettes. (Anthony Abbott)

The King of Pain, an A-10 assigned to the 354th FS, Myrtle Beach kept a record of her ground kills in the form of silhouettes and numbers. The King of Pain accrued additional radar kills before the Gulf War ended. (Fred Schlenker III)

74

Have Gun, Will Travel was an A-10 (79-224) assigned to the 511th TFS at RAF Alconbury , UK. (Anthony Abbott)

(Above Right) A-10 (81-947) *Desert Belle* of the 511th TFS returned from the Persian Gulf and was given fresh make-up for an airshow. (Anthony Abbott)

FREE KUWAIT was one of two 511th TFS A-10s to also carry the name BROTHERS IN ARMS. (Anthony Abbot)

(Right) The Bullet Express! (78-592) was flown by the 354th TFW Commander, Colonel Sandy Sharpe. (Anthony Abbott)

The 917th Tactical Fighter Wing at Barksdale AFB, Louisiana also created the 'Peanut Scheme' for possible use during OPERATION DESERT STORM. in late 1990. This A-10 was the sole example of the scheme and was painted FS33105 Field Drab, FS33303 Sand, and FS 33245 Earth Yellow. The Peanut Scheme was also ordered removed before the aircraft deployed.

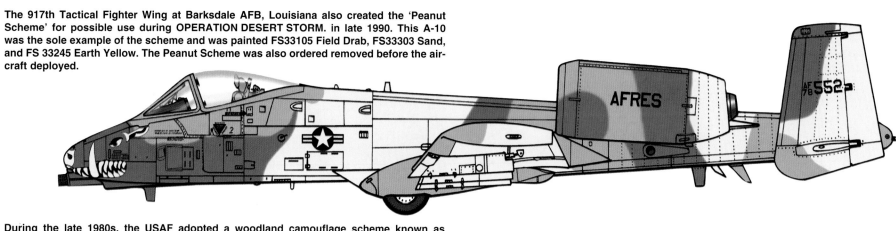

During the late 1980s, the USAF adopted a woodland camouflage scheme known as European I. The camouflage consisted of FS34092 Dark Green, FS34102 Medium Green, and FS36081 Dark Gray and was optimized for use in western Europe. This A-10 was assigned to the 81st TFW, RAF Bentwaters-Woodbridge, UK.

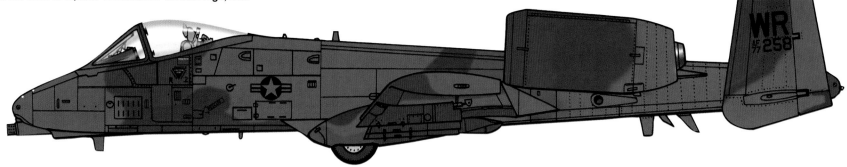

This A-10 was assigned to the 23rd TFW, England AFB, Louisiana when it was sent to the Persian Gulf in 1990 to take part in OPERATION DESERT STORM. The aircraft wore a red, white, and black sharkmouth over the nose — emulating the markings used by the unit in China during WW II.

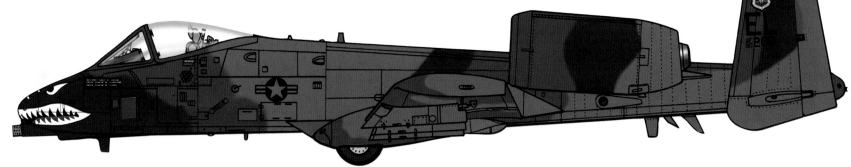

The 906th TFW was a USAF Reserve unit flying out of New Orleans Naval Air Station, Louisiana when it was sent to the Persian Gulf in 1990.

CHOPPER POPPER was flown by Captain Robert Swain of the 906th TFG when he shot down an Iraqi Bo-105 helicopter on 6 February 1991. Capt Swain was temporarily assigned to the 23rd TFW (Provisional) when he scored his kill — the first A-10 and first gun kill of the Gulf War.

The USAF began to revert to a two-tone gray scheme during the early 1990s when the A-10 was given the dual role of close air support and Forward Air Controller. The gray scheme, FS36320 Dark Ghost Gray and FS36375 Light Ghost Gray, was designed to improve the effectiveness of the camouflage at a variety of altitudes. This A-10 was assigned to the 510th FS, 52nd FW, Spangdahlem AB, Germany in 1992.

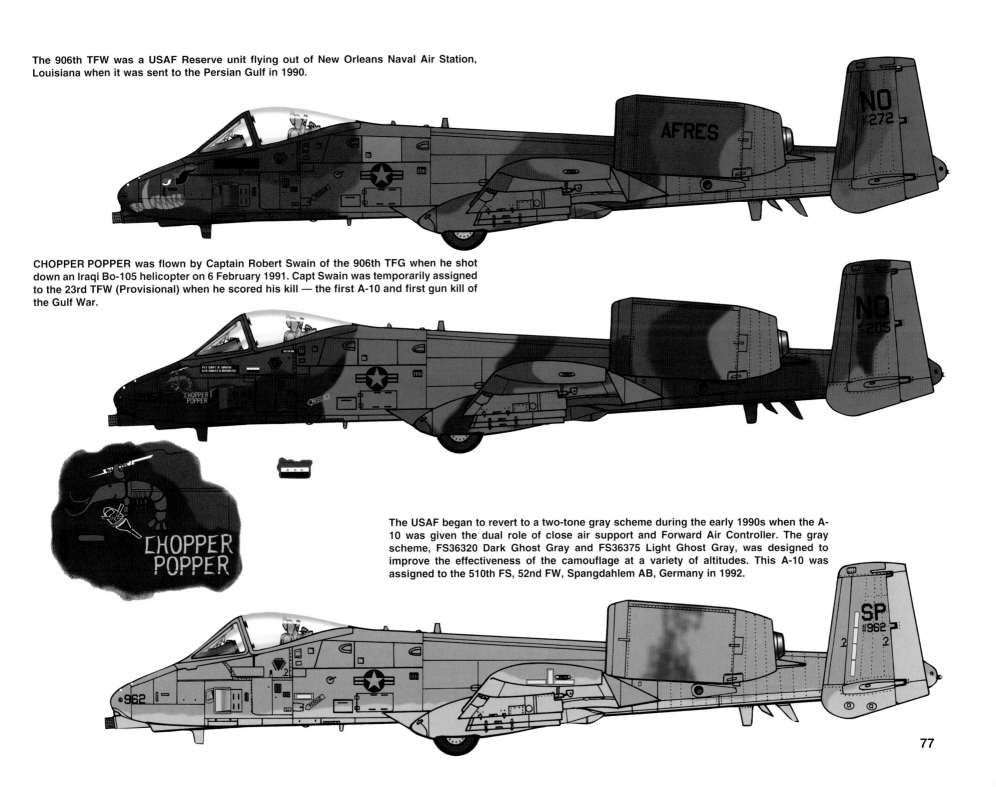

Two 23rd TFW A-10s were photographed just before their departure for OPERATION DESERT STORM in 1990. The aircraft at left (80-224) was assigned to the 74th TFS, 23rd TFW, however the A-10 at right (82-662) was transferred to the 353rd TFS (Myrtle Beach). (Ken Kubik)

In 1980 the 47th TFS, 917th Tactical Fighter Group (TFG), Air Force Reserve, became the first AFRes unit to the receive the A-10. The 47th TFS continues to the fly the 'Hog although the green and gray European I camouflage scheme has given way to the more recent two-tone gray scheme. (R. Van Dorst)

(Above) The demise of the Warsaw Pact and subsequent drawdown of USAF units in Europe has resulted in the formation of composite units designed to cover a wide variety of tactical missions. These range from low-and-slow ground attack to high speed strike, interdiction, and interception missions. The 52nd Fighter Wing operated the A-10 in the 81st FS (ex-510th FS) and the Lockheed/General Dynamics F-16C in the 22nd and 23rd FSs. The Wing's 53rd FS operates the McDonnell-Douglas F-15C Eagle. (C. Knowles)

(Below) This 23rd TFW 'Flying Tigers' A-10, based at King Fahd International Airport, Saudi Arabia, is equipped with four AGM-65 Maverick missiles, a pair of LAU-68 rocket launchers, an ALQ-119 ECM pod, and a pair of AIM-9L Sidewinders — a typical Gulf War weapons load. This firepower, often delivered in an up-close and personal manner, contributed greatly to the mass surrenders of Iraqi troops during the Gulf War. Such mass surrenders by troops of an opposing field army had not been seen since the collapse of Nazi Germany in March and April of 1945. An A-10 ancestor, the Republic P-47 Thunderbolt, was involved there as well. (Robert V. Pease)

79

Also from squadron/signal publications

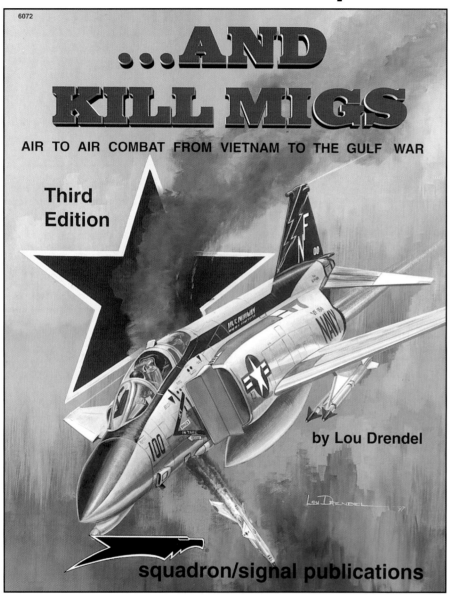

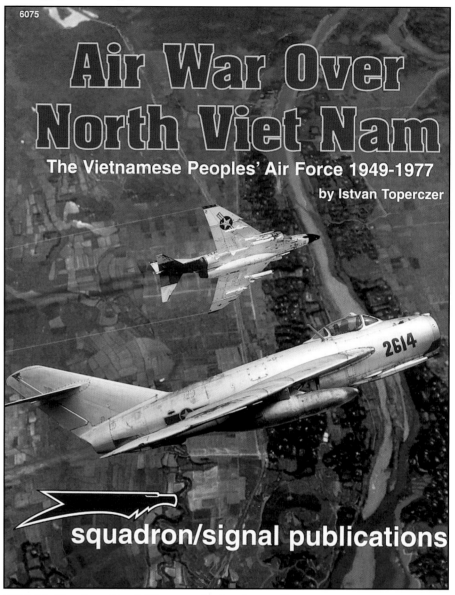

6072 ...AND KILL MIGS. Author Lou Drendel uses both official and personal accounts to bring the reader into the cockpit of USAF and US Navy fighters as they engage enemy fighters over the steaming jungles of Vietnam and the burning sands of the Middle East. Extensively illustrated with color and black and white photographs and color paintings. 104 pages, 16 pages of color.

6075 Air War Over North Vietnam. Author Istvan Toperczer, conducting extensive research into the the files of the Vietnamese Peoples' Air Force, as well as conducting personal interviews, tells the other side of the story of the air war over North Vietnam. This book is an exciting, and perhaps controversial, account of MIGs engaging wave after wave of US fighters and bombers. Illustrated with color and black and white photos and color paintings. 64 pages.